Support comes from The Fetzer Institute whose mission
is to foster awareness of the power of love and forgiveness
in the emerging global community.
fetzer.org

HARDEST PART OF LOVE
Music and Lyrics by Stephen Schwartz
Copyright © 1989, 1998 Grey Dog Music (ASCAP)
International Copyright Secured.
All Rights Reserved.
Administered by Williamson Music.

Evangel Press, 2000 Evangel Way, Nappanee, Indiana

Summary: Letting go of a child is the hardest part of love,
but it is also the rarest and truest.

ISBN 978-1-933858-37-1

Library of Congress Control Number: 2008924309

First edition

Orders: (574) 773-3522

For Scott & Jessica Schwartz
and Summer & Cybil Stillson

"... I think you would agree
You're newer here than me..."

"The Tree of Knowledge"
Children of Eden

Oh this child of mine I love so well
and oh the toil it takes

would build a bridge of dreams for him
and patch it where it breaks

But the one thing he most treasures
is to make his own mistakes O h O h O h

 e is bound for lands I've traveled
I remember them so clear

I could
 tell him
what to
  watch for

I could
 warn him
what to fear

could shout until I'm breathless
and he'd still refuse to hear O h O h O h

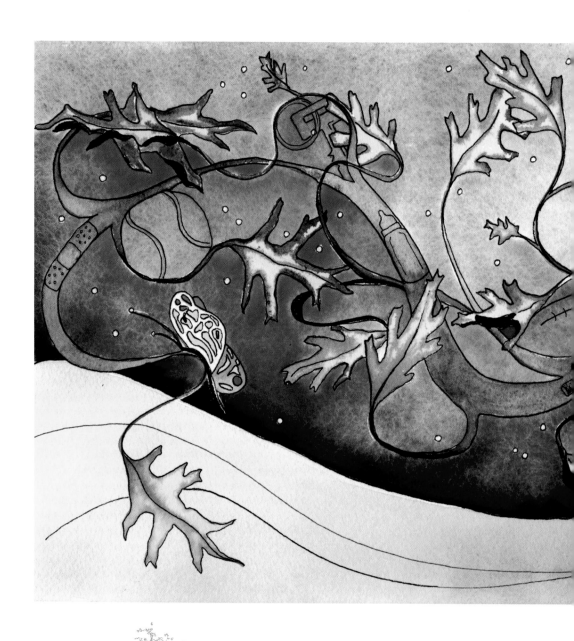

 ut you cannot close the acorn
once the oak begins to grow

nd you cannot close your heart
to what it fears and needs to know

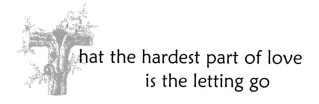That the hardest part of love
is the letting go

s a child I found a sparrow
that had fallen from its nest

...nd I nursed it
back to health
till it was stronger
than the rest

ut when I tried to hold it
then it pecked and scratched my chest
till I let it go

nd I
watched it
fly away from me
with its bright
and selfish song

16

nd a part of me was cursing
    I had helped it grow so strong

nd I feared it might go hungry
and I feared it might go wrong O h
O h O h

But you cannot
close the acorn
once the oak
begins to grow

And you cannot close your heart
    to what it fears and needs to know

hat the hardest part of love
is the letting go

And it's only in Eden
  grows a rose without a thorn

And your children start to leave you
　　　on the day that they are born

They will
leave you there
to cheer for them
they will
leave you there
to mourn ever so

Like an ark on uncharted seas
their lives will be tossed

And the
deeper is your
love for them
the crueler
is the cost

nd just when they start to find themselves
is when you fear they're lost O h O h O h

But you cannot close the acorn
once the oak begins to grow

And you cannot close your heart
to what it fears and needs to know

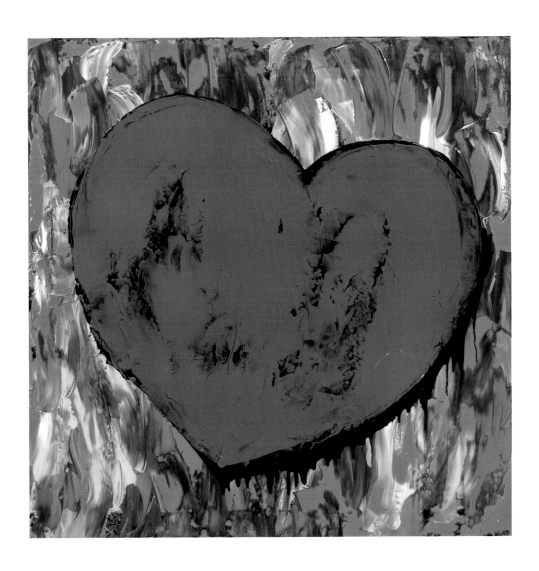

That the hardest part of love

And the rarest part of love

And the truest part of love

Love   Is letting go

"All Done!"

"The Naming"
Children of Eden

Erwin, North Carolina
KAREN BEITAR has been creating art since childhood. When she was diagnosed with a muscle disorder in 2001 and could no longer work a full-time job outside the home, she started painting whenever she was able. Her artwork is inspired by different cultures, folk tales, history, music, poetry, travel, and memories. She resides in a small mill town located on the beautiful Cape Fear River. kfbart.bravehost.com

Chicago, Illinois
HANNAH GRABER graduated from Goshen College in Goshen, Indiana, where she studied art. She is interested in continuing to pursue illustration and book arts. Music usually becomes a part of her art as the ideas and sounds from songs influence her drawing process. Birds and squares are Hannah's favorite things to draw. hannah.graber@gmail.com

Goshen, Indiana
DEE BIRKEY holds an Associate Degree in commercial art. She has held positions as advertising agency art director, in-house designer for a public relations team, and pre-press operator and designer for a printing company. Today she has her own studio, Design Directions, specializing in computer-generated marketing collateral. Married to her high school sweetheart, they have four adult children (a son, daughter, and their spouses) and three grandkids. Lucas served as her model and "is the epitome of the lyrics." bydesigndirections.com

Island Lake, Illinois
TIM S HOOKER draws humorous illustrations using bold lines and bright colors. He has dabbled in all mediums and feels most at home with pen and ink, pencil, watercolor, and acrylics. After receiving his B.F.A. from Northern Illinois University, he worked on the island of Guam as art director for Hyatt Hotels and Resorts. He began his own freelance business in 2000, Crayon Pie Studios, and recently painted a larger than life mural for The Onion Pub in Barrington, Illinois. caconline.org

Bremen, Indiana
JESSICA FLORES has "always needed to create." Hanging in her studio is a snapshot of a little freckle-faced redhead atop a tricycle; dirt smeared on her cheeks and hair flying in all directions. It reminds her to get messy, use her imagination, and not only color outside the lines, but draw new ones. Jessica is exploring the urban craft movement and plans to design fabrics and papers of her own. She enjoys sharing her art in her family's studio loft and works at the Nappanee Public Library. As a new mom, she is sharing the joy of daughter, Nora, with her husband, Dan. jessicaflores.com

Anchorage, Alaska
ANN LYNN was born and raised in southern California. She earned her biology degree at the University of California at Riverside and taught middle school science for fourteen years. In a leap of faith, her family - husband and two sons - moved to Frankfort, Indiana, and more recently, Anchorage, Alaska. Thus freed from the bounds of a "real job" she runs her own business, Annie's Handmade Jewelry, specializing in one-of-a-kind wirework, beadwork, lampworked glass, and polymer clay sculpture pieces. anniesjewelry.com

Dedication

South Bend, Indiana
BIRDIE ROSSOW MCELROY
grew up in St. Louis, Missouri.
For many years she taught
primary children from Chicago
to the United States Virgin
Islands, all the while finding
creative expression in the visual
arts. She has specialized in
major concept design, creating
thematic works around a
dominant motif - including a large scale triptych for
the Saint Joseph Regional Medical Center and a
painting commissioned by the National Fischoff
Chamber Music Association. The YWCA of St. Joseph
County voted her Woman of the Year for Arts,
Literature, and Culture. She is represented by the
Craig Smith Gallery in Harbert, Michigan. Birdie lives
with her husband, Jerry, and son, Chris. Her married
daughter, Jacqui, lives in Florida. birdieart.com

South Bend, Indiana
SHIRLEY NATOLI was born in
Paterson, New Jersey, but lived
many years in Venezuela, her
mother's birthplace. She is an
Indiana University graduate
concentrating in sculpture,
painting, and drawing. In
addition to an internship for the
movie, *Dork of the Rings*, she
has been a design manager and
relief sculptor for a cosmetics company, an animator,
published illustrator, and costume technician plus
archivist assistant at the University of Notre Dame
and gallery monitor at the South Bend Regional
Museum. Her son, Michael, lives in Chicago pursuing
an acting and directing career. natoli2@yahoo.com

Chicago, Illinois
JAMES MCNEILL MESPLE is a
prolific and active fixture in the
Chicago art world, painting
brilliantly-colored mythological
works set along the edges of
Chicago and its lakefront. Before
painting begins, a finish coat of
gesso, a plaster-like substance,
is applied to the canvas. The
translucent quality of Mesple's
personally made mixture of oil and egg tempera-
based pigments allows light to reflect from the gesso
increasing the depth and luminosity of the paintings.
Originally from the Missouri Ozarks, he attended
the University of Missouri before moving to Chicago
and graduating from Northeastern Illinois University
in 1970, later studying under Karl Wirsum at the
School of the Art Institute of Chicago.

South Bend, Indiana
RAMIRO RODRIGUEZ was born
to Mexican emigrants and grew
up in western Michigan. He
attended Fennville Public Schools
and graduated with a B.F.A. from
Kendall College of Art and
Design in 1990. He received his
Master of Fine Art Degree from
the University of Cincinnati,
Ohio. Ramiro is an exhibition
coordinator at the Snite Museum of Art at the
University of Notre Dame where he lives with his
wife and sons. His figurative prints are in the permanent
collections of the Mexic-Arte Museum in Austin, Texas,
and the Art Museum of South Texas. He has
encountered the widest public recognition through
the reproduction of his works by the multi-platinum
selling musical group, *Tool*. ramirorodriguez.com

Winona Lake, Indiana
NICOLE MOORE is an artist
and designer who believes in
living life artfully. She creates
art that evokes a sense of
wonder, joy, and whimsy.
As a fashion design major in
college, she tested the waters
of many mediums and crafts.
Since college she has lived and
worked everywhere from New
York City to Shanghai, China, and traveled to many
places in between. In addition to doing art fairs, she
opened her own gallery, Art & Soul, at The Village
at Winona. artandsoulshop.etsy.com

New York, New York
JESSICA SCHWARTZ teaches
middle and high school art
on the Upper West Side. She
photographed and designed her
father's *Reluctant Pilgrim* and
Uncharted Territory CDs as well
as Scott Coulter's self-titled CD
for LML Records. She has worked
as the in-house designer for The
Acting Company and created
identity design logos for Riot Entertainment and the
United Nations. Her photographs could be seen on
the set of *Bat Boy the Musical* at the Union Square
Theater in 2001. Jessica has worked with celebrity
and fashion photographers Theo Westenberger and
Paul Rackley. She continues to build a strong body of
mixed media paintings, and as Stephen Schwartz's
daughter, providing illustrations for a song about his
children has been a project close to her own heart.

Photo by Josh Dirlam

Mooresville, Indiana
DOUG SMITH is a husband of more than twenty-five years, father of two, and a freelance illustrator living near Indianapolis, Indiana. While working full time for a major service organization, he also pastors a small church and has a life-long commitment to doodling on every scrap and corner of blank paper available. Doug and his family enjoy traveling whenever possible and being outdoors, whether camping, hiking, or fishing. douglsmith912@aol.com

19

Stow, Ohio
TODD VOLKMER is a lifelong northeast Ohio native and an energetic multi-tasker in life and in art. He's a prolific painter who works on several canvases at once - each in a different style. Todd's paintings always pulse with color, movement, and his zest for life. To market his work, Todd created iSmudge, an on-line art gallery that now features the work of more than 1,000 artists from around the world. He is owner and curator of Red Light Galleries in the Northside Arts District in Akron, Ohio, and director of CityArtProject.org. toddv.com

7   **29**

Nappanee, Indiana
JEFF STILLSON devotes much of his time as graphic designer for Amish Acres historic farm and tourist attraction listed in the *National Register of Historic Places*. Many outdoor murals throughout the heritage town and rural county have been hand painted by Jeff to beautify the community and resurrect local pride. He finds time to coach youth basketball, softball, and soccer and owns Stillson Studio of Advertising & Design, Inc.

Cover Art, Book Layout & Design

Dayton, Ohio
RACHELLE LEE WITTER (Chelle) is a graduate of Bethel College in Mishawaka, Indiana. Semesters abroad took her to Ecuador and Oxford, England, where she studied art and medieval history. She is an art teacher who loves to travel, play the piano, and read - simultaneously. 320.artistportfolio.net

6   27

Wilmore, Kentucky
LAURA URY studied art in California at Long Beach City College and then San Jose State University. She completed her B.A. Degree in studio drawing and painting at Asbury College in Wilmore, Kentucky, in 1983. Although her focus has been oil painting, Laura has worked to develop her skills in a variety of mediums in order to realize her lifelong dream of being an illustrator for children's books and Christian publications. She has taught for more than fifteen years and spent three years as an adjunct instructor at Bethel College's Art Department in Mishawaka, Indiana. She lives in Hong Kong with her husband, Dr. Thane Ury, where she teaches art at the International Christian School. Laura has four children. upologist@aol.com

26   28

Crown Point, Indiana
LAURA ZATO-CLEMONS' love of art and affinity for drawing and painting was apparent from an early age. A descendant of Czechoslovakian and Hungarian heritage, Laura comes from a long line of accomplished artists, musicians, and writers. She graduated from the American Academy of Art, Chicago, Illinois, in 1990. She works as the communications specialist for the Crown Point Community Library and as a freelance illustrator as well as portrait photographer specializing in children and newborns. Her inspiration comes from husband, Joel, and children, Dylan and Lauren. zdsart@ameritech.net

9